THE GOOD, THE BAD & THE QUEEN

Published by
Wise Publications, 14-15 Berners Street, London, W1T 3LJ, UK.

Exclusive distributors:
Music Sales Limited, Distribution Centre, Newmarket Road,
Bury St Edmunds, Suffolk, IP33 3YB, UK.

Music Sales Pty Limited, 120 Rothschild Avenue, Rosebery, NSW 2018, Australia.

Order No. AM989703 ISBN: 978-1-84609-991-5
This book © Copyright 2007 Wise Publications, a division of Music Sales Limited.

Edited by Fiona Bolton. Music arranged by Jack Long.
Music processed by Paul Ewers Music Design.

Original cover design by Will Bankhead.
Cover image, detail from The Tower and the Mint;
painting by T. Sotter Boys in the mid-nineteenth century.

Printed in the EU.

www.musicsales.com

WISE PUBLICATIONS
PART OF THE MUSIC SALES GROUP

London / New York / Paris / Sydney / Copenhagen / Berlin / Madrid / Tokyo

HISTORY SONG

Words & Music by Damon Albarn & Paul Simonon

don't know it now, _____ then you will do. _____   If you

don't know it now, _____ then you will do. _____

Northern Whale

Words & Music by Damon Albarn & Paul Simonon

1. An-oth-er wave crash o - ver you,___ it put you in a spell

But a north-ern whale would-n't leave_____

{ you un - til old Eng - land's }
{ _ you un - til all our } tears are done, and the day_

comes.___ We move_____ on_

end - less - ly._____

80's Life

Words & Music by Damon Albarn & Paul Simonon

11

Kingdom Of Doom

Words & Music by Damon Albarn & Paul Simonon

We'll let it blow _____ a - way,

yeah._____ *Instrumental till end*

Behind The Sun

Words & Music by Damon Albarn & Paul Simonon

look - ing at the peo - - - ple we've be - come.

To a place where you played when you were young

on the cool breeze be - hind the sun.

1.

The Bunting Song

Words & Music by Damon Albarn & Paul Simonon

1. Pull out the bunt - ing,_____ she made 'em one by
3. Bye, Ba - by Bunt - ing, all Eng - land wants you

Nature Springs

Words & Music by Damon Albarn & Paul Simonon

set - ting   course___ to   a   land   un - der___   me.___
look - ing   for___   a   dream___   far   a - way.___

A Soldier's Tale

Words & Music by Damon Albarn & Paul Simonon

Three Changes

Words & Music by Damon Albarn & Paul Simonon

(2°) 1. Call-ing up   the sounds,_   you out   there on___ the seas:

vic - tim.

Special effects inserted here

GREEN FIELDS

Words & Music by Damon Albarn & Paul Simonon

The Good, The Bad And The Queen

Words & Music by Damon Albarn & Paul Simonon

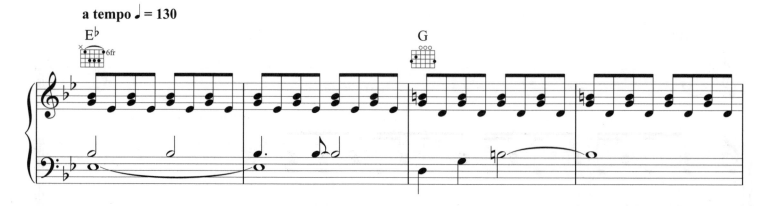

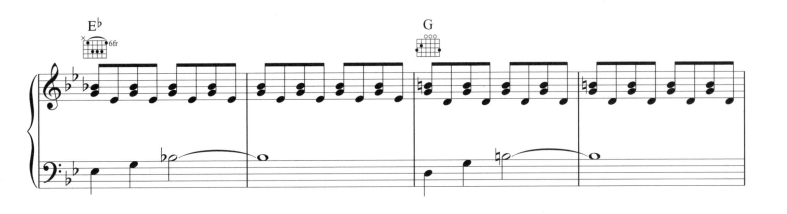

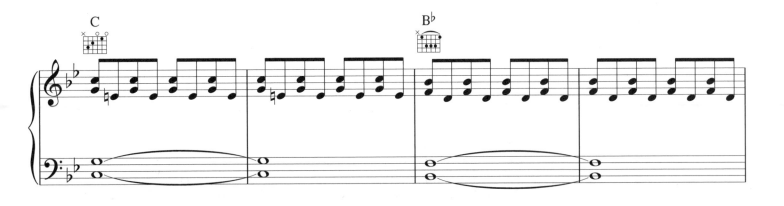

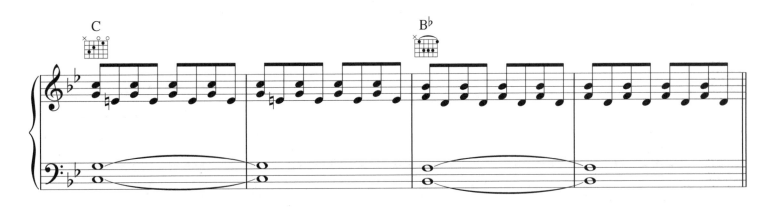

1. Mov-ing up - town, but I know it's the part that I should be; the
(2.) bless-éd rou - tine for The Good, The Bad And The Queen: just

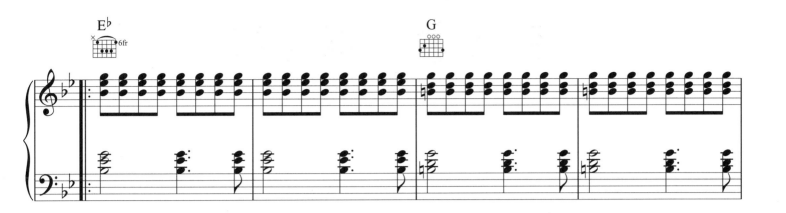

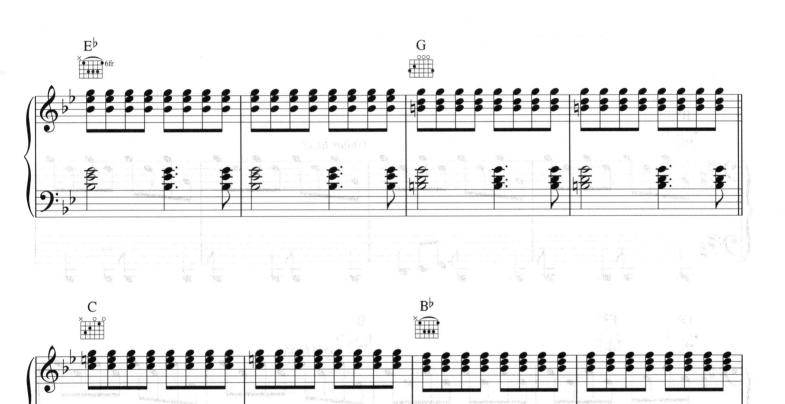

Repeat ad lib.

Back In The Day

Music by Damon Albarn & Paul Simonon

Herculean

Words & Music by Damon Albarn & Paul Simonon

1. Stand-ing by the old ca-nal   by the gas___
2. The call for pray'r is com-mon round here   in the morn-